All Around the Town

ALL AROUND THE TOWN

By Phyllis McGinley

Illustrated by Helen Stone

J. B. LIPPINCOTT COMPANY

Philadelphia & New York

PRINTED IN THE UNITED STATES OF AMERICA

Twelfth Printing

Library of Congress Catalog Card No. 48-7865

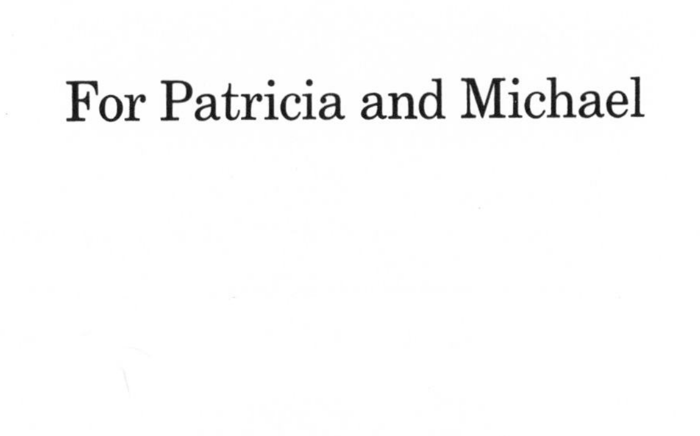

For Patricia and Michael

Other Books
by Phyllis McGinley and Helen Stone

THE HORSE WHO LIVED UPSTAIRS

THE PLAIN PRINCESS

THE MOST WONDERFUL DOLL
IN THE WORLD

THE HORSE WHO HAD HIS PICTURE
IN THE PAPER

LUCY McLOCKETT

THE YEAR WITHOUT A SANTA CLAUS

THE MAKE-BELIEVE TWINS

BLUNDERBUS

East Side,
West Side,
  Everywhere you look,
City sights
Are witty sights
  And bursting for a book.

So here's a little list of them
  Arranged from A to Z
The gay things,
The stray things
  That city children see.

A

A is for the Aeroplane.
 Ah, watch it soar and sail!
It likes to carry passengers,
 It loves to carry mail.
And sometimes in the afternoons,
 It's apt to advertise
And write amusing messages
 Across the city skies.

PEPSI COLA

B

B's the Bus,
The bouncing Bus,
  That bears a shopper store-ward.
It's fun to sit
In back of it
  But seats are better forward.
Although it's big as buildings are
  And looks both bold and grand,
It has to stop obligingly
  If you but raise your hand.

C is for the Circus
Which springtime brings to town.
(The country has its crocus,
But we much prefer the clown.)
C's for canes and cracker-jack
And curious camels, too.
I wouldn't trade a Circus
For some crocuses. Would you?

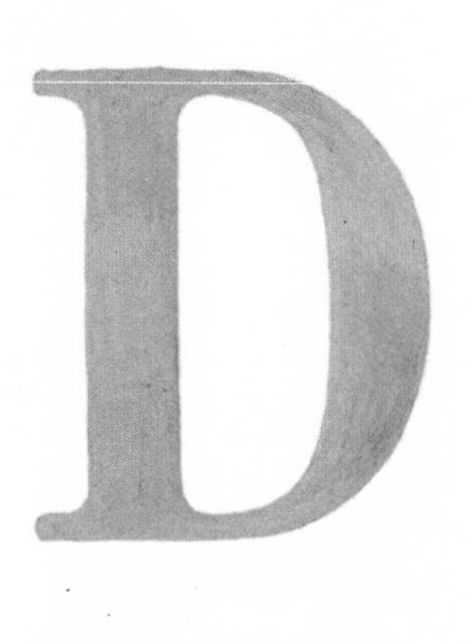

D's the Dairy Driver.
He makes a daily round
With milk that tastes delicious
Or with butter by the pound.
And even eggs by dozens
He'll deliver at the door.
I do believe the Dairyman's
Our favorite visitor.

E is the Escalator
  That gives an elegant ride.
You step on the stair
With an easy air
  And up and up you glide.
It’s nicer than scaling ladders
  Or scrambling ’round a hill,
For you climb and climb
But all the time
  You’re really standing still.

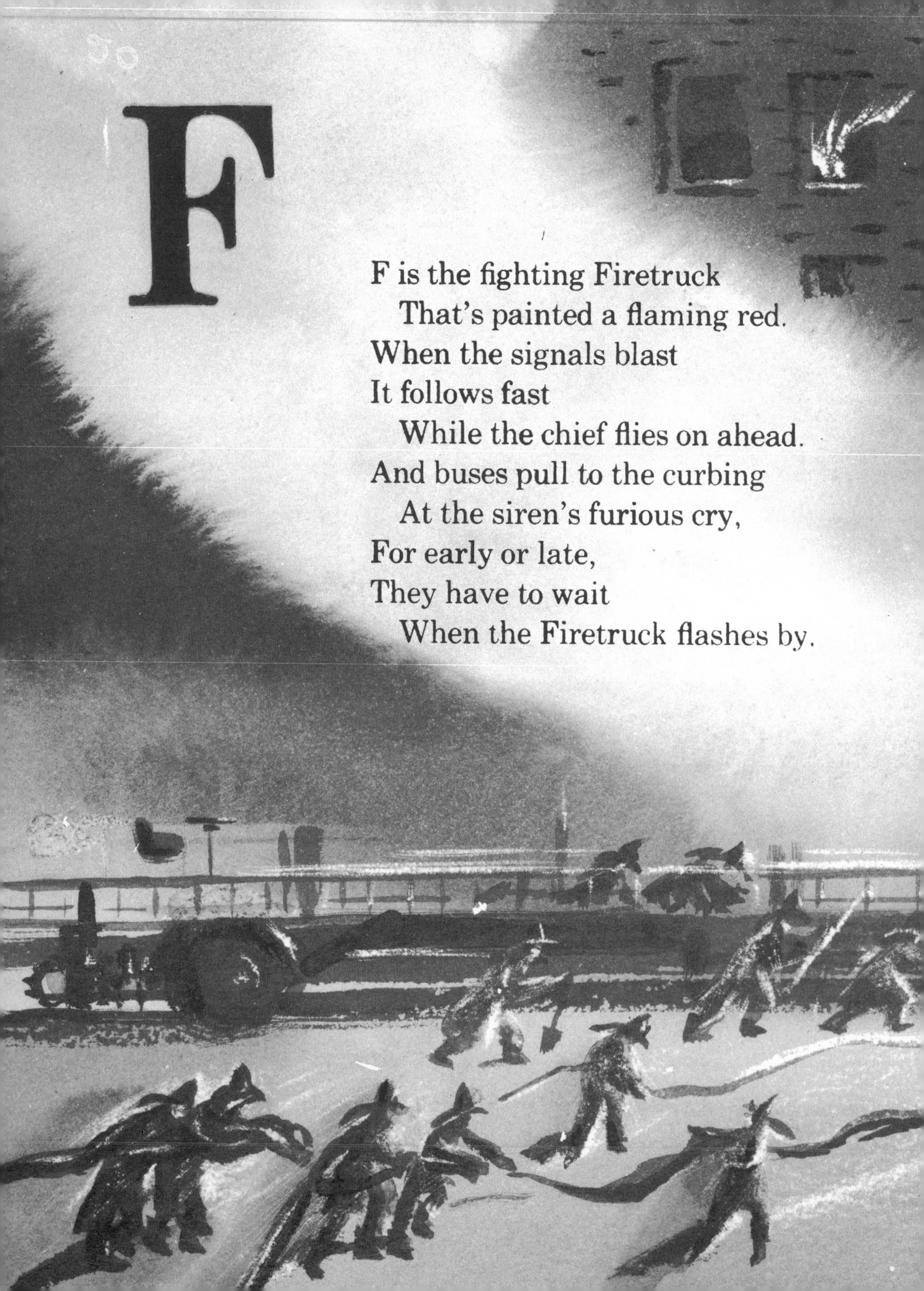

F

F is the fighting Firetruck
  That's painted a flaming red.
When the signals blast
It follows fast
  While the chief flies on ahead.
And buses pull to the curbing
  At the siren's furious cry,
For early or late,
They have to wait
  When the Firetruck flashes by.

G

G's the gay Good-Humor man
  Who gads about the block.
Good gracious! when he rings his bell,
  How all the children flock!
They leave their games to gather 'round
  And gravely take their pick
Of chocolate or vanilla
    Or of orange-on-a-stick.

H

H is for the Horses
That haul their city loads.
They feel at home on avenues
Instead of country roads.
They wear a hat in summertime,
A blanket when it ends.
They like a carrot handout.
And the pigeons are their friends.

NO
RIDE
PD

I's for Ice on skating rinks
  That glimmers cold and pearly
Where people's skates
Cut figure-eights
  And people's skirts are twirl-ey.
It must be nice
Around the Ice
  To glide so smooth and clean—
Not flying and not dancing,
  But just something in-between.

J

J's the jumping Jay-walker,
  A sort of human jeep.
He crosses where the lights are red.
  Before he looks, he'll leap!
Then many a wheel
Begins to squeal,
  And many a brake to slam.
He turns your knees to jelly
  And the traffic into jam.

K

K's for Kindergarten
  Where you learn all kinds of things
Like coloring or making kites
  Or paper-crowns for kings.
And maybe you're already there,
  Or maybe you are waiting
Till you are five,
Or—sakes alive!—
  Perhaps you're graduating.

U.S.
MAIL

L is for the Letter-box—
The place to leave a letter.
Perhaps if it leaned lower down
You'd love it even better.
But since it likely will not learn
To shrink the littlest bit,
You'll have to grow and grow until
You're tall enough for it.

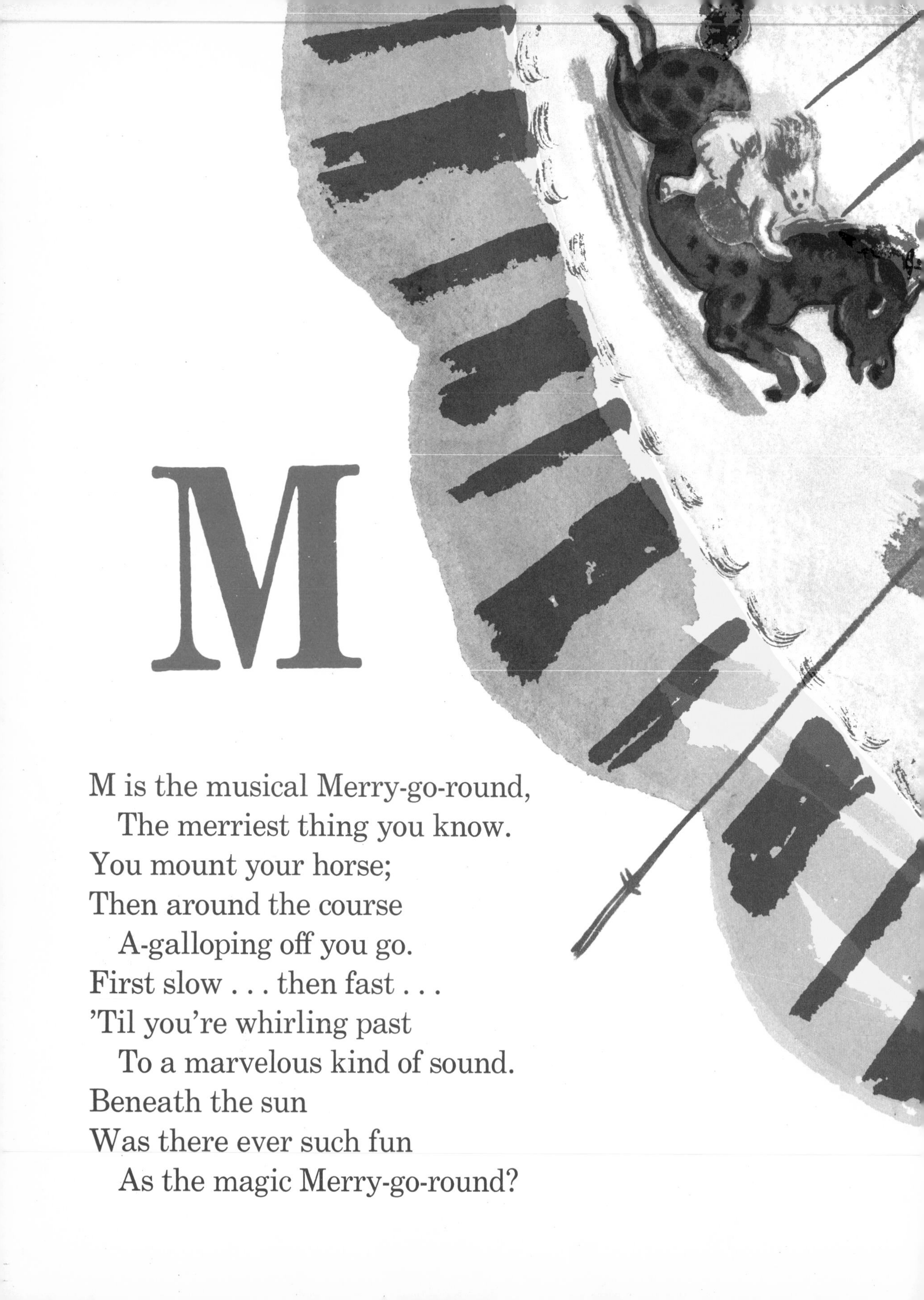

M

M is the musical Merry-go-round,
The merriest thing you know.
You mount your horse;
Then around the course
A-galloping off you go.
First slow . . . then fast . . .
'Til you're whirling past
To a marvelous kind of sound.
Beneath the sun
Was there ever such fun
As the magic Merry-go-round?

N

N's for next-door Neighbors
Whom you hardly know at all.
They live upon the floor above
Or just across the hall.
Try not to be too noisy
At your night-and-morning games,
For your Neighbors are your Neighbors
Though you never learn their names.

O

O's the Organ-grinder.
When he opens up with tune
You're sure that winter's over
And that kites are coming soon.
So fetch your hoops and roller-skates
And wear an April mind.
If the grinder grinds his Organ
Can the spring be far behind?

P

P's the proud Policeman
With buttons polished neat.
He's pleased to put his hand up
When you want to cross the street.
By daylight he protects you;
He protects you through the dark,
And he points the way politely
To the playground or the park.

Q is for the Quietness
  Of Sunday avenues
When silence walks the city
  In her pretty velvet shoes;
When trucks forget to rumble,
  And from steeples everywhere
The bells of Sunday morning
  Ring their questions on the air.

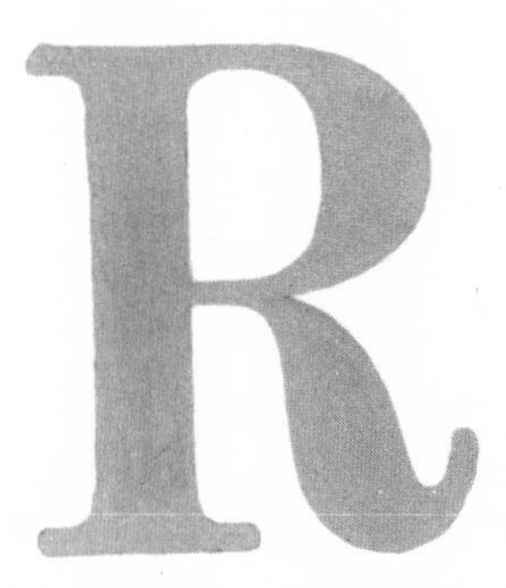

R is for the Restaurant—
  A really special treat.
(We do respect the relative
  Who takes us there to eat.)
The waiters rush with plates of rolls,
  They run to hold one's chair,
And always seem
To read ice-cream
  Upon the bill-of-fare.

S

S is the snorting Subway
  That slithers below the ground.
It's sort of a scaly dragon.
  It roars with a dragon sound.
And sometimes far
In the foremost car
  The motorman lets you stand
To see the place
Where the dragons race
  Through their dark and shivery land.

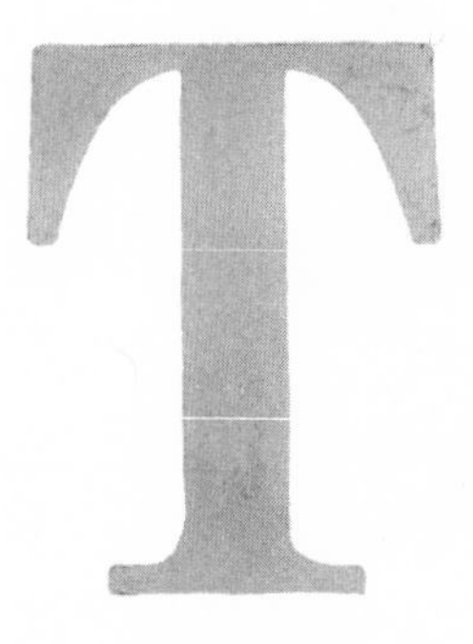

T's the ticking Taxicab
   That's faster than a trolley.
It answers to a whistle
   Like a terrier or a collie.
I think we'd always travel
   In a taxi to and hence—
But to tell the truth about it
   It's a terrible expense.

CAB NO.
DRIVER MAY STOP SHORT
.065
FARE

U is for Umbrellas
That bloom in rainy weather,
Like many-colored mushrooms,
Sprouting upward altogether.
How useful an umbrella is!
But still I often wonder
If a roof on stormy evenings
Isn't nicer to be under.

V

V is for the Vendor
   A very vocal man.
He drives about in summer
   With a vegetable van.
And everybody listens
   To his voice upon the breeze,
Calling "Strawberries, Strawberries!
   Fresh green peas!"

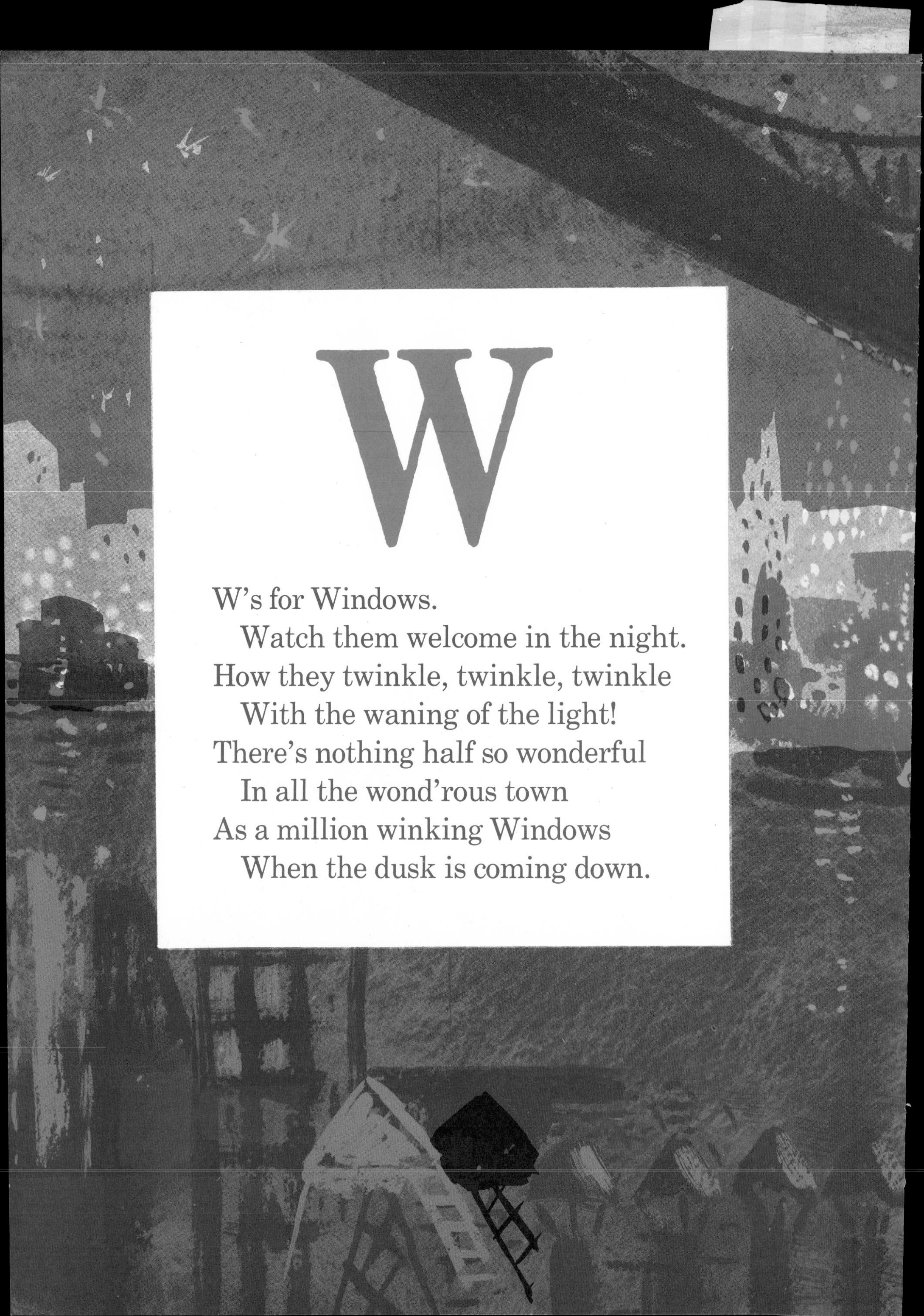

W

W's for Windows.
  Watch them welcome in the night.
How they twinkle, twinkle, twinkle
  With the waning of the light!
There's nothing half so wonderful
  In all the wond'rous town
As a million winking Windows
  When the dusk is coming down.

CKEY MOUSE
PLA
PEANUTS

X

X is 'Xcavation.
When a building's being made,
It's almost as exciting
As an extra big parade.
So even busy grown-ups
Will stand in pouring rains,
Examining the dump-trucks
And the shovels and the cranes.

Y? Well, Y's for Your house—
Your yard,
Your roof,
Your wall.
Though yonder lies the rest of town,
Your own is best of all.
It's where your mother yearningly
At evening tucks you in,
And where todays turn yesterdays
Before they half begin.

Z

Z must end the alphabet.
  It's never in the middle.
So let's have fun before we're done
  And make this one a riddle.
Z's the place, the lovely place,
  You always go with zeal
To watch the zigzag zebra
  And the tiger and the seal,

The tall giraffe who makes you laugh,
The birds of fancy feather
And polar bears from frigid zones
That love the zero weather,
The camel and the llama
And the hippo and the gnu.
Oh, Z's the best of all the rest.
Of course, you've guessed —

THE ZOO